Noon
Sight
Navigation

Simplified
Celestial

by ARTHUR A. BIRNEY

Design & Illustrations by
E. James White

**CORNELL
MARITIME
PRESS**

Centreville, Maryland

Library of Congress Cataloging in Publication Data

Birney, Arthur A   1927-
    Noon sight navigation.

    1. Nautical astronomy.   I. Title.
VK555.B63   527   72-88042
ISBN 0—87033—171-X

To
the sea, the wind, the stars
and Alison

NHU 11/80   _CMP0053_

_7.00_

Contents

Introduction	4
Equipment	6
Dead Reckoning	6
Time Calculation	10
Zone Time	10
Time Zones	11
Sun Time	12
Greenwich Time	12
Radio Time Signals	15
Use of a Sextant	15
Instrument Error	18
Dip	18
Refraction	20
Artificial Horizon	22
Longitude	22
Problems	29
Latitude	29
Latitude from the Noon Sight	30
Plotting	38
Problems	39
Time of Meridian Passage	39
Taking the Time	40
Moon Shots	41
Answers to Longitude Problems	44
Answers to Latitude Problems	45
Tables	
Excerpt from the _Nautical Almanac_	46
Increments and Corrections	47

Introduction

This little book offers an extremely simple, accurate and fast method of establishing one's position at sea. It can be read easily in an hour and any sailor of average competence should be able to use the method herein described without difficulty once he has read it.

Noon sight navigation is not a new concept. It has been used and proven by many mariners since Captain Cook began his famous voyages in 1768; it is practical and it works. The essentials are presented here in a fresh and easily understood series of steps which lead to the quick determination of a position.

This booklet is not intended as a course in basic piloting or seamanship, nor is it intended to be the ultimate authority on celestial navigation. It is intended for the reasonably experienced skipper who for various reasons has not learned complete celestial navigation but may from time to time find himself offshore and wondering where in the World he is. In the event of the navigator's sudden illness or if he should jump ship in Tahiti, the procedures here described will bring both ship and crew home safely. And, really, that is all that one can ask.

The obvious merits of this system are its simplicity and speed. Its major drawback is that it can only be used at one time during the day—at local apparent noon (LAN), when the Sun is at its highest. If the Sun or the horizon should be obscured at that particular moment, the opportunity for a noon sight is lost until the next day.

Most experienced navigators use the noon sight to establish latitude but few seem to realize that longitude can be obtained as well. Beyond the requirements of the usual latitude sight, it is only necessary to take the time and to follow the procedure detailed to obtain longitude.

Even though we know that the Earth spins on its axis daily while traveling around the sun annually, for our purposes, as practical navigators, we shall consider the Sun as circling the Earth, as this is what appears to happen. Thus, the Sun seems to rise in the East each morning, to travel across the sky and to set in the West each evening.

Equipment

To navigate successfully one needs certain basic equipment. This includes a proper ship's compass, parallel rules, dividers, a sextant, an accurate timepiece, charts, plotting sheets and a current *Nautical Almanac.* * A radio receiver capable of picking up time signals is also highly desirable as it will permit ship's time to be maintained to the second. The importance of extremely accurate time will be seen later.

Dead Reckoning

Dead reckoning is the art of establishing a position at sea by drawing a course line on a chart from a known location in the direction of one's compass course and marking off on this line the distance traveled over a given period of time. Distance is determined by multiplying estimated speed by the time traveled. The term "dead reckoning" is probably derived as a contraction of the expression "deduced" or "ded." reckoning. Accurate dead reckoning (DR) is the single most important element in successful navigation. Columbus discovered America with nothing more than DR and with it he returned to his landfalls in the New World on the three voyages following his Great Discovery. When all else fails for the navigator (and you may rest assured that from time to time all else will fail), he will have his DR to fall back on.

If one were to sail from Sandy Hook at New York Harbor at 10:00 A.M. on a true course of 90° maintaining a speed of six knots, he would

*The *Nautical Almanac* is available at many marine stores or may be ordered directly from the Superintendent of Documents, U.S. Government Printing Office, Washington, D.C. 20402.

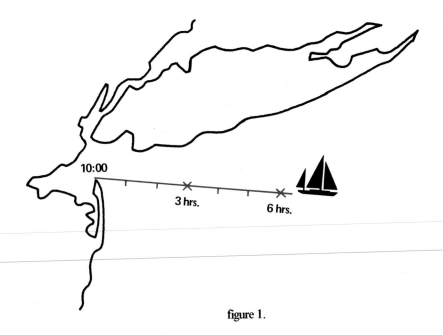

figure 1.

be exactly 18 miles due east of Sandy Hook at the end of three hours; 24 miles out at the end of four hours, and so forth. This is dead reckoning in its simplest form.

Setting up the DR and making sure that proper entries are regularly made are primarily the navigator's, but ultimately the skipper's, responsibilities. Where there are separate watches, as in ocean racing, the navigator should explain precisely what is needed to the watch captains and at frequent regular intervals plot the information entered in the rough log by the watch as a DR position on the chart or plotting sheet. An entry should be made in the log at least every half hour indicating the time of the entry and the course and speed averaged during the previous half hour. In addition, of course, the exact time of any change of course should be noted.

Errors creep into the DR position as a result of currents, leeway, inaccurate estimates of speed, storms which render estimates of speed and course difficult and various other factors. *Noon Sight Navigation* offers a method of correcting the DR position by an accurate celestial fix once each day. With an accurate fix you can correct the DR and start from a known position each day at noon. This prevents a cumulative error from building up and serves as an invaluable check for the navigator.

No doubt about it, Columbus would have given his shirt if he could have known exactly where he was just once a day!

Estimating
Speed
Speed through the water is a deceptive matter to estimate. On yachts equipped with logs or speedometers which have been accurately calibrated, the problem is simplified. Beware, however, of relying exclusively on any piece of electronic or mechanical gear, for the ocean environment has a way of corroding and making inoperable even the best of equipment. It is a good idea to develop a sense of speed.

A man can walk comfortably at about three miles per hour. Using this fact as a basic reference one can with practice learn to judge the speed of a boat through the water quite accurately.

It is most important that one gain proficiency in judging boat speed under various conditions. Often sailors overestimate their speed on the wind and underestimate it when running free. This is probably because the heel of the boat when close-hauled gives a feeling of speed, while sitting upright when running and with the apparent wind reduced, makes one feel that the wind has lessened and that the boat has slowed down.

Another interesting method of measuring your boat's speed through the water is by noting with a stopwatch the seconds required for a chip of wood, crumpled paper towel, or the like to travel a given distance. The procedure here is to measure either 30 or 40 feet along the deck forward from the helmsman. One person then drops the marker over the side calling "Mark" as it hits the water. The helmsman starts the stopwatch at that moment and stops it as the object passes him.

Obviously, the greater the distance which the marker travels the more accurate will be the results. The following tables give speeds in knots for both 30-foot and 40-foot distances.

30 Feet	40 Feet
6 Seconds = 2.9 Kn	8 Seconds = 2.9 Kn
5 Seconds = 3.06 Kn	7 Seconds = 3.3 Kn
4 Seconds = 4.4 Kn	6 Seconds = 3.9 Kn
3 Seconds = 5.9 Kn	5 Seconds = 4.7 Kn
2 Seconds = 8.8 Kn	4 Seconds = 5.9 Kn
	3 Seconds = 7.7 Kn
	2 Seconds = 12 Kn

However one obtains his information it must periodically be plotted on the chart as a DR position and it is the DR position which forms the basis for all celestial navigation.

Time Calculation

Before going further, let us consider what time is and three different kinds of time which affect the navigator.

In essence, time is a measured portion of eternity. On Earth we have chosen to use as our basic measuring interval the period of one revolution of the Earth, or one day. The day, of course, we have divided into 24 equal parts, or hours. To avoid confusion with A.M. and P.M. time in navigation, we use a 24-hour time system which shows 1:00 P.M. as 1300, 2:00 P.M. as 1400, and so forth. Noon is thus 1200 and midnight 2400.

Zone Time

For convenience in our daily living, we have established 24 "time zones" around the world. Each of these is 15° wide (the distance the Sun appears to travel across the sky in one hour) and we have decreed that the same time shall prevail throughout each time zone. Thus the time shown on all watches and clocks within a particular zone should be the same even though the Sun will pass over the eastern boundary of the zone almost one hour before it passes over the western boundary.

Figure 2 is a diagram of the 24 time zones as shown on a cross section of the world as viewed from the South Pole. Each 15° meridian marks the center of a time zone. Each zone extends 7½° on each side of its 15° meridian. A new day begins at Greenwich when the Sun crosses G_1, the International Date Line. Hours of difference from Greenwich time are shown in circles. This difference is called the "zone description."

Time Zones

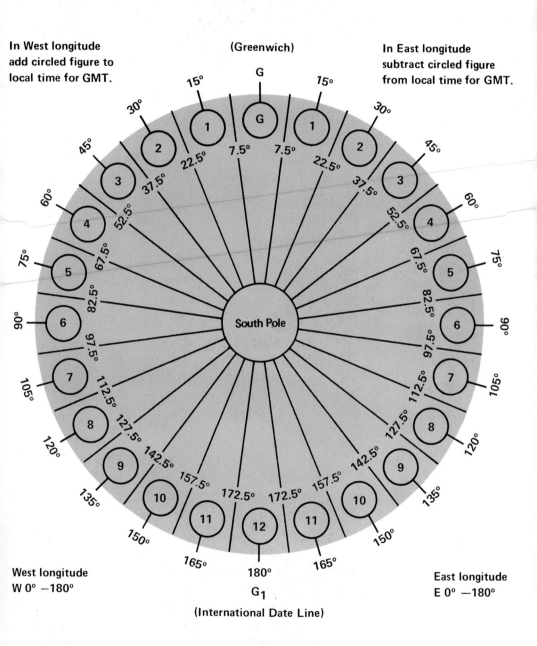

In West longitude add circled figure to local time for GMT.

(Greenwich)

In East longitude subtract circled figure from local time for GMT.

West longitude
W 0° −180°

South Pole

East longitude
E 0° −180°

G_1
(International Date Line)

figure 2.

"Daylight Saving Time" is, of course, simply a modified form of zone time. When it is in effect, clocks are set forward one hour so that there will be longer periods of light in the evening. This results in a reduction by one hour of all zone descriptions. For example, the zone description for W. 73° on Standard Time would be 5. On Daylight Saving Time, it would be 4.

Sun Time

Sun time is determined by the position of the sun relative to your location on the surface of the Earth. Local noon by Sun time thus occurs at the exact moment when the sun is on your meridian, i.e., when the Sun is due North or due South of you. This moment is also known as "meridian passage" or "local apparent noon" (LAN). All other Sun time is calculated from that basic reference.

If we were to regulate our lives strictly by Sun time, chaos would result for, as we have seen, the Sun is constantly moving across the heavens. For this reason, only other people on our precise same meridian of longitude would share our exact time. This is impractical because those a few miles east would see the Sun rise and meridian passage occur, a few minutes earlier than those further west (assuming that the horizon were unobstructed by hills, trees and buildings). Sun time in any given location is thus a very precise sort of time as the Sun can be in only one place at any given moment.

Greenwich Time

Greenwich time is the time in Greenwich, England. It is a form of timekeeping most useful to us, for it is the time shown in the *Nautical*

Almanac as GMT—Greenwich Mean Time.

When the "average" Sun passes over the meridian of Greenwich, England, it is noon there. When it passes over the meridian on the exact opposite side of the World (the International Date Line) it is midnight in Greenwich and a new day starts there.

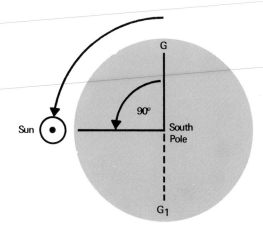

figure 3.

In the diagram above, we are looking at the South Pole of the Earth from a vantage point in space. The Sun will always be depicted as traveling counterclockwise. If it is over G (Greenwich) at noon and will be over G_1 (International Date Line) at midnight, the diagram must represent 6:00 P.M. in Greenwich, or halfway between noon and midnight.

In the above diagram, it can also be seen that the Sun has traveled one quarter of the way around the Earth, or 90° of the circle.

If the Sun were over G_1, the Sun would be 180° from Greenwich.

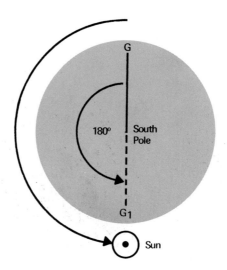

figure 4.

Thus it may be seen that Greenwhich time may also be expressed in terms of the degrees of a circle from the Greenwich Meridian.

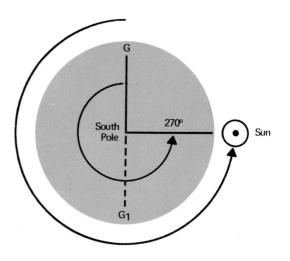

figure 5.

This is the "Greenwich Hour Angle" or "GHA" which the Sun has traveled. Greenwich time may be converted into an equivalent number of degrees of angle, or arc, quite simply by using the first table in the back of the *Nautical Almanac*, "Conversion of Arc to Time." This table is reproduced in the back of this book.

Radio Time Signals

Radio time signals are broadcast day and night by the United States on 2.5, 5, 10, 15, 20 and 25 MHz with voice broadcasts every five minutes. Canada also broadcasts a strong signal on 6.3 megacycles and every five minutes on 3.330, 7.355 and 14.640 kHz. With these signals the navigator's watch can be set precisely to the correct time or any variation noted.

Use of a Sextant

Basically, the sextant is merely an instrument with which one can measure angles with great accuracy. With it one can measure the angle between the horizon, himself and a celestial object. In essence, it is little more than a sophisticated protractor.

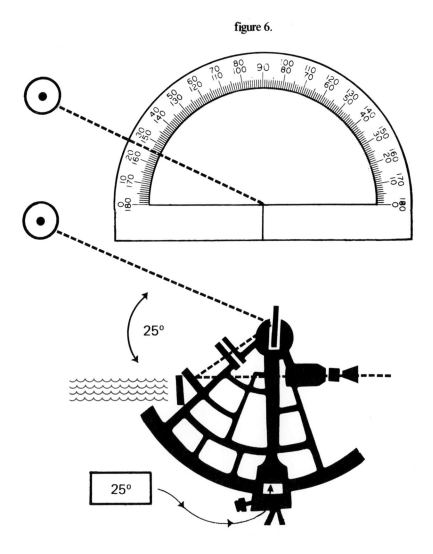

figure 6.

If we could hold a protractor level and measure the angle of the Sun with it we would obtain the same information which the sextant gives us. The sextant, of course, enables us to measure much more accurately than we ever could merely with a protractor. The sextant is also a delicate instrument and must be handled with great care lest it be damaged.

Mounted in front of the telescope or sighting tube of a sextant is a piece of glass, one side of which is transparent, the other mirrored. In sighting through the sextant the horizon should be centered in the clear side of this "horizon glass" and the sextant's index arm disengaged and moved to "bring down" the celestial object until it just kisses the horizon. Once the object has been brought down near the horizon by disengaging the arm and moving it, the arm should be re-engaged and the fine tuning adjustment used for the greatest precision. Finally, while adjusting the fine tuning device the sextant should be rocked in a slight arc from left to right to be certain that the object just touches the horizon and that the instrument is being held vertical. If the instrument is not vertical when the sight is taken, an error in the measurement will result.

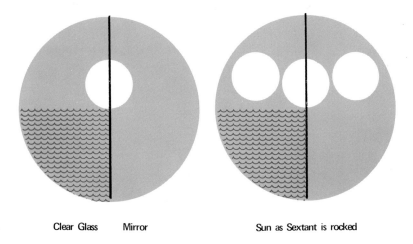

Clear Glass   Mirror   Sun as Sextant is rocked

figure 7.

Normally, the bottommost edge is brought to the horizon. This is known as the *lower limb* of the body. if we wish we can use the topmost edge or *upper limb*. Stars and planets have no visible diameter and are thus merely brought to the horizon as points of light. See Fig. 10.

The raw sight which is obtained directly from the sextant is commonly called the "height shot" or H.S. The H.S. must be corrected for several factors before it is useful to us.

Instrument Error

In looking through the telescope or sighting tube of a sextant the horizon may appear broken in the middle of the field of view when the index arm is set at zero. By careful adjustment the horizon can be made to become a single continuous line. When the horizon appears as a straight line the sextant should read exactly zero. If it does not, note the amount of the error and whether it is above or below zero. If it is above zero, the instrument will be reading that much too high in any observation and a correction must be made in the H.S. to account for this. This is known as "instrument error" or "i.e."

Obviously, if the sextant is giving readings which are too high, the error will be deducted from the reading on the instrument. If it is giving readings which are too low, the instrument error should be added.

Dip

Another necessary correction is for the Dip or height of eye above the water. The horizon appears to dip away as one gets higher above the water so we must compensate for this.

There is a table of the correction for Dip inside the front cover of the *Nautical Almanac*.

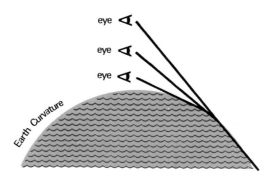

figure 8.

Height of eye is given in both meters and feet so be sure to use the correct scale. The height of your own eye should be added to the height of the deck above the water to determine the correct "height of eye" with which to enter the table. On most medium-sized yachts this will total approximately 10 feet, for a dip correction of 3.1 minutes of arc. The dip correction is always subtracted from the H.S. Part of this table is shown below.

ION TABLES 10°-90°—SUN, STARS, PLANETS

	STARS AND PLANETS				DIP				
Upper Limb	App. Alt.	Corrⁿ	App. Alt.	Additional Corrⁿ	Ht. of Eye	Corrⁿ	Ht. of Eye	Ht. of Eye	Corrⁿ
′	° ′	′		**1972**	m	′	ft.	m	′
21·2	9 56	−5·3		**VENUS**	2·4	−2·8	8·0	1·0 − 1·8	
21·1	10 08	−5·2		Jan. 1–Feb. 29	2·6	−2·9	8·6	1·5 − 2·2	
21·0	10 20	−5·1		0°	2·8	−3·0	9·2	2·0 − 2·5	
20·9	10 33	−5·0		′	3·0	−3·1	9·8	2·5 − 2·8	
20·8	10 46	−4·9		42 +0·1	3·2	−3·2	10·5	3·0 − 3·0	
20·7	11 00	−4·8		Mar. 1–Apr. 15	3·4	−3·3	11·2	See table	
20·6	11 14	−4·7		0°	3·6	−3·4	11·9	←	
20·5	11 29	−4·6		47 +0·2	3·8	−3·5	12·6	m ′	
20·4	11 45	−4·5		Apr. 16–May 12	4·0	−3·6	13·3	20 − 7·9	
20·3	12 01	−4·4		0°	4·3	−3·7	14·1	22 − 8·3	
20·2	12 18	−4·3		46 +0·3	4·5	−3·8	14·9	24 − 8·6	

Refraction is another correction that must always be applied to one's H.S. Light rays entering the Earth's atmosphere from a celestial body bend as they approach Earth just as a stick appears to bend when thrust into the water. The lower the angle at which light rays enter the atmosphere the greater the bending.

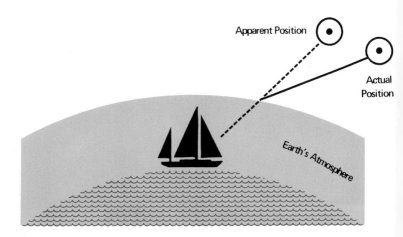

Apparent Position

Actual Position

Earth's Atmosphere

figure 9.

The first table inside the front cover of the *Nautical Almanac*, "Altitude Correction Tables 10°-90°" and "0°-10°" gives the corrections for refraction. Be sure to use the proper column, Oct.-Mar. or Apr.-Sept. and enter the table with the value of your "Apparent Altitude," that is your H.S. corrected for dip and instrument error. This table also makes allowance for the fact that the center of the Sun is not sighted but either its lower or upper limb is brought to the horizon, so care must also be used to make sure that the proper column for Upper or Lower Limb is used. Lower limb sights always give a +

figure 10.

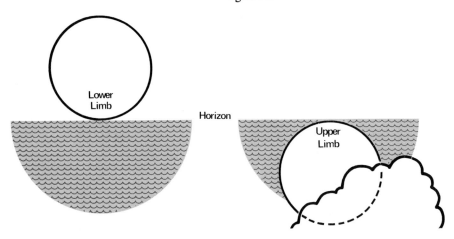

correction; upper limb sights always give a — correction.

The upper limb sight is most often used with the Moon when it is in a crescent phase but it will occasionally be useful with the Sun in the event its lower limb is obscured by a cloud.

The above three corrections must always be made to any sextant readings. When they have been applied, the H.S. becomes the *Height Observed*, or H.O.

The following form will be useful in finding the total correction to apply to the H.S. to obtain H.O.

H.S.   _____
i.e. (+ or —)   _____
Dip (—)   _____
_____

App. Alt.   _____
Alt. Corr. (+ or —)   _____
_____

H.O.   _____

Example. Find H.O. from H.S. (sextant reading) of 43° 16' on lower limb, height of eye 10 feet with instrument error of +3', date January 1, 1972.

H.S.	43° 16'	
i.e.	−3'	
Dip	−3.1	
App. Alt.	43°10'	(Enter Alt. table with this
Alt. Corr.	+15.2	argument)
H.O.	43°25'	

Artificial Horizon

If the open sea is not readily available for practice sights, a shallow pan of water may be used as an artificial horizon. Place the pan so that the Sun's image can be seen reflected in it. Sight the image in the water in the clear side of the frame and bring down the Sun in the sky in the usual way. Using this system, however, the two Suns are superimposed on each other to form one disc instead of one being brought to the horizon. No correction for dip is used; other corrections as usual. H.S. is then halved to obtain apparent altitude and from this H.O. is obtained. If the wind disturbs the water too much, light oil, such as kitchen cooking oil, may be substituted.

Longitude

Distance around the world, East and West, is called *longitude.* It is measured East or West of Greenwich, England which marks the zero meridian. Meridians are imaginary lines which radiate from the North Pole like spokes in a wheel and extend due South to the South Pole.

Values of meridians increase as one goes East or West from Greenwich until one reaches the International Date Line, which is 180° from Greenwich. Each degree (°) of longitude is composed of 60 minutes (') and each minute of 60 seconds ("). It is thus possible to state with precision exactly how far East or West one is from the Greenwich Meridian in terms of longitude East or West.

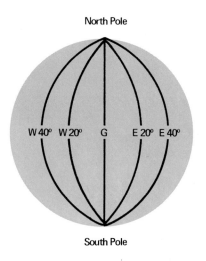

North Pole

W 40° W 20°   G   E 20° E 40°

South Pole

Meridians of Longitude Side View of Earth

figure 11.

The angle between Greenwich, the center of the Earth, and the Sun is constantly changing as the Sun circles the Earth. This angle is known as the *Greenwich Hour Angle* (GHA) and is stated in continuously increasing values from zero at Greenwich to 359°+ as the Sun approaches Greenwich from the East. Longitude on the other hand, is never expressed in values of over

180° as it switches from West to East at the International Date Line and at Greenwich. In all of the following diagrams we are viewing the South Pole of the Earth and the Sun is traveling counterclockwise.

figure 12.

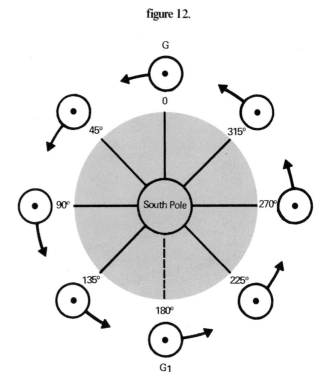

Various Greenwich Hour Angles of the Sun

The Sun travels at approximately 15° each hour so that in each 24-hour day it makes one complete circle of 360° around the Earth.

If the Sun traveled at a uniform rate of speed it would cross the Greenwich Meridian at precisely 12:00 noon each day. Unfortunately, the Sun does not travel at a uniform speed, and so from day to day there are variations in the

figure 13.

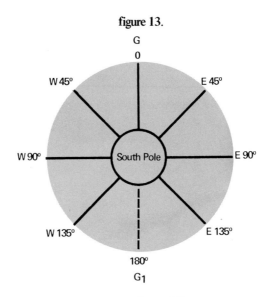

Longitudes, East and West

exact time when it crosses the Greenwich Meridian. This variation from the average is called the "Equation of Time" and it represents the difference between the average time of meridian passage and the precise time when it occurs on a particular day.

By *meridian passage* is meant the exact moment when the Sun or other body is on our meridian; i.e., when it lies due South or due North of us. Up until that moment the body will have been ascending in the sky. After it, it will be descending.

figure 14.

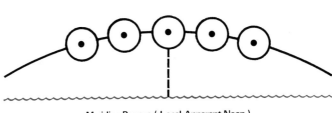

Meridian Passage (Local Apparent Noon)

The Sun is at its highest point in the sky and will be either due South or due North of the observer as he faces it.

If you will examine a typical page from the *Nautical Almanac*, as reproduced on p. 46, you will note the first column on the right-hand page to be G.M.T., Greenwich Mean Time.

The second broad column is headed *Sun* and is divided into two parts, G.H.A. and Dec. Dec. refers to *declination* and is explained in the Section on latitude. G.H.A. means *Greenwich Hour Angle*. You will note that the G.H.A. is always at its lowest near 1200. This is because the Sun would be directly over Greenwich at noon but for the Equation of Time.

figure 15.

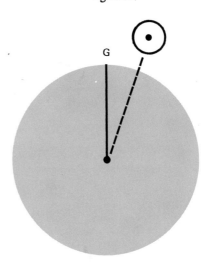

Equation of Time places Sun late at 1200

GHA = 358° 41'

If we had an accurate timepiece on board our vessel and were able to time the precise moment

figure 16.

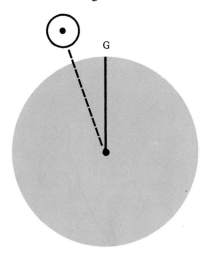

Equation of Time places Sun early at 1200

GHA = 3° 57′

of meridian passage of the Sun, we could by a simple computation establish our longitude.

For example, on January 1, 1972, we know that we are somewhere in the North Atlantic and our DR gives us a longitude of 63° West. With the sextant we take the time of the Sun's meridian passage at $12^h 03^m 21^s$.

It is now important to determine what time it is in Greenwich. As shown in Figure 2, the World is divided into 24 time zones. Each time zone is 15° wide and extends 7.5° on either side of a 15° meridian.

Since our DR places us at approximately 63° W., we can see from Figure 2 that we are in the 4th zone, or that it is exactly four hours later in Greenwich than it is where we are. Thus the GMT of our meridian passage was $12^h 03^m 21^s$ + 4 hours or $16^h 03^m 21^s$.

Now look down the GMT column in the *Nautical Almanac* for January 1, 1972 to the 16th hour and note the GHA. It is shown as 59°09.6'. Since the time shown is for whole hours we must add to the value shown for the 16th hour the value of the additional 03^m21^s.

The second table in the back of the *Almanac* is entitled "Increments and Corrections." Each page gives the values for two minutes of time in separate columns and shows also the cumulative value of each additional second. To use this table simply turn to the page with the number of minutes with which we are concerned (in this case 3) and run down the $\frac{Sun}{Planet}$ column to 21 seconds. This is shown as 0°50.3'. This increment is then added to the value obtained for the even hour and we have our longitude.

59°09.6'   [whole hour GHA]
+ 0°50.3'   [Increment for 3^m21^s]
50°59.9'   West — This is our longitude.

If you were in East longitude at the time of your sight it would be necessary to convert your GHA into East longitude by subtracting your GHA from 360°. Remember that GHA is expressed as an angle increasing continuously from zero at Greenwich to 359°+ as Greenwich is approached from the East. Since longitude is never expressed in terms of over 180° it is necessary to subtract any GHA of more than 180° from 360° to obtain East longitude. Thus, if the Sun's GHA were 270° at the time of your sight, you would be at 90° East. See. Figs. 12 & 13.

Determine longitude from the following:

1. January 2, 1972   DR Long. W.   121°16'
   Time of LAN   12:10:05

2. January 1, 1972   DR Long.E.   61°08'
   Time of LAN   11:59:22

(Answers on page 44.)

---

atitude

If you will examine a world globe you will notice the Equator as the large band circling the Earth midway between the North and South Poles. Parallel to the Equator and also circling the Earth above and below it are additional bands representing the degrees of *latitude*. These increase in value as one moves either North or South from the Equator in a range from 0°, the Equator, to 90° at either the North or South Poles. Each degree of latitude is made up of 60 minutes and each minute of 60 seconds. It is thus possible to state precisely how far North or

figure 17.

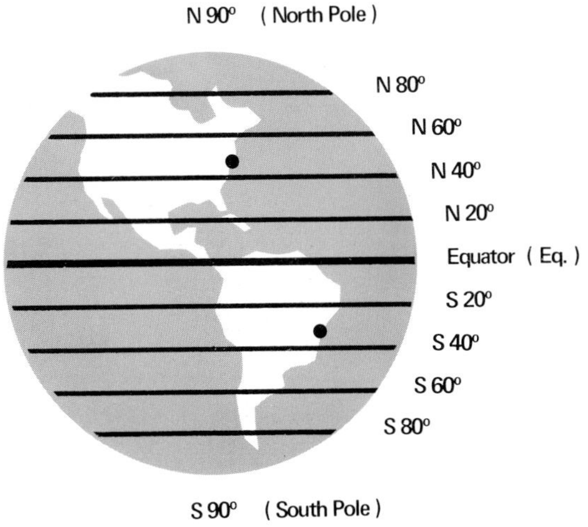

N 90°   (North Pole)

N 80°
N 60°
N 40°
N 20°
Equator (Eq.)
S 20°
S 40°
S 60°
S 80°

S 90°   (South Pole)

South of the Equator one is located in terms of degrees (°), minutes (') and seconds (") North or South.

For example, Washington, D.C. is located at N.38°50', New York lies at N.40°30', and Buenos Aires, Argentina at S.34°40'.

Latitude from the Noon Sight

Declination (Dec.) is simply the number of degrees North or South of the Equator at which a celestial body may be found. When it is summer in the Northern Hemisphere, the Sun has a North Declination and it is winter in the Southern Hemisphere.

figure 18.

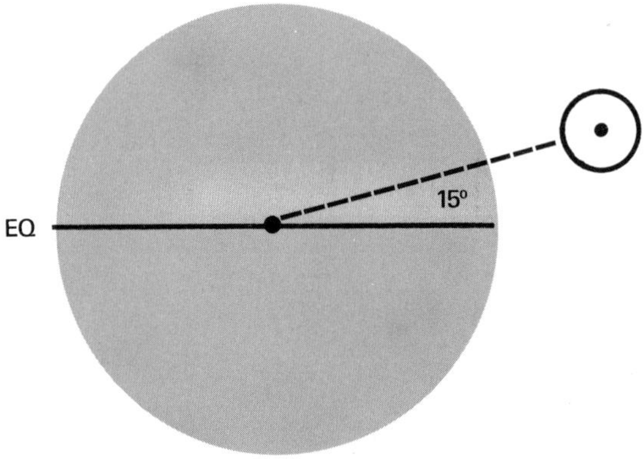

Here the Sun has a declination of 15° North

As we have seen, the *Nautical Almanac* gives the Declination of the Sun and Moon for each whole hour of GMT throughout the year. Since Declination changes much more slowly than the hour angle it is not necessary to interpolate between the hours for minutes and seconds, but

figure 19.

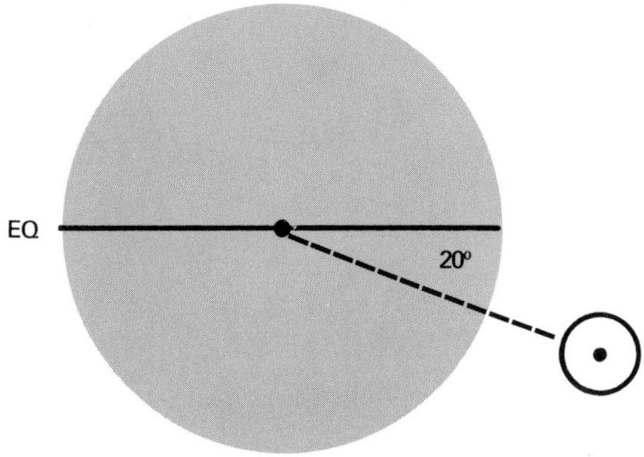

Here the Sun has a declination of 20° South,
thus it is summer in the Southern Hemisphere
and winter in the Northern Hemisphere.

it is sufficient simply to use the Declination
given for the nearest whole hour to the time of
your sight.

At Local Apparent Noon (LAN) we can
obtain latitude directly from a Sun sight. To do
this we need know only the H.O. of the Sun at
meridian passage and its Declination. If, with a
sextant, we follow the Sun as it ascends in the
sky and note the greatest value that it achieves
before beginning to descend, we can determine
our latitude with only the *Nautical Almanac*.

At the moment of our shot we are actually
standing at a point on the Earth's surface (L)
(Latitude) and the horizon we see as we look
forward is a line which is tangent to the Earth
Circle at that point.

The Sun is so far from Earth that there is no
appreciable difference in an observation of the
Sun, a Star or Planet from either L or C, the
center of the Earth. Therefore, we can draw C H

figure 20.

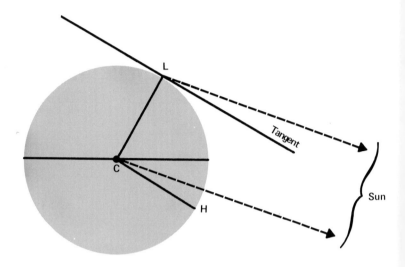

parallel to the tangent line and use C H in our diagrams rather than the tangent line, as this makes the diagram simpler. Since two parallel lines crossing a straight line form equal angles, the use of C H rather than the tangent line will not affect the rest of the diagram.

For example, let us suppose that it is January 1, 1972, and that we are somewhere off the East Coast of the United States. Let us assume that the highest corrected reading we obtained from our sextant, our H.O., as we followed the Sun up to meridian passage was $18°26'$. We can now construct a simple diagram which will graphically demonstrate how to obtain our latitude.

We will first draw a circle with a line running through it representing the Earth and the Equator, with a dot representing center of the Earth. Let us assume that all angle lines to be drawn will terminate at the Earth's center, C.

figure 21.

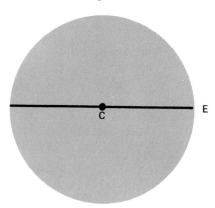

Next, we add the Sun, S, in the location of its approximate Declination either North or South. This declination we obtain from the daily pages of the *Nautical Almanac*. For January 1, 1972, at 1200 the Declination is shown as S 23°03.3'. We shall drop the fraction of a minute for convenience and sketch in the Sun at an angle below the Equator (since the Declination is South) of approximately 23°03'.

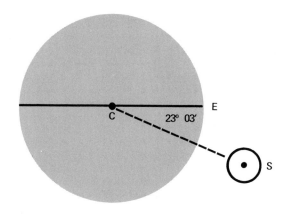

figure 22.

Next, place a mark, L, on the diagram at approximately your DR latitude. If you bear in mind that the topmost and bottommost points of the circle represent the North and South Poles and that there are 90° between each of them and E, you should have no problem in marking this approximate latitude. For example, 45° is halfway between a pole and the Equator, 30° is one-third of the distance, and so forth.

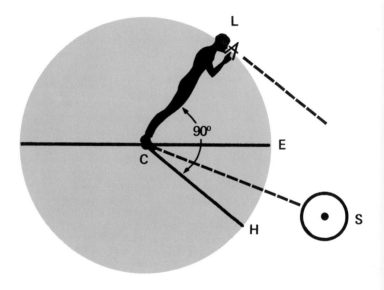

figure 23.

Now draw a line from L to C and then a line at a 90° angle to this line from C to the Earth Circle. Mark the point where this last line meets the Earth Circle H. This line represents your horizon.

The final step in the construction of the diagram is to place in the angle SCH the H.O. you obtained from your sextant reading.

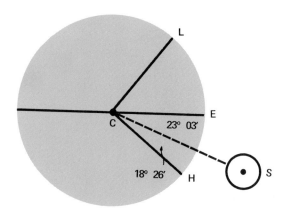

figure 24.

Simple addition and subtraction will now give us the latitude. We know the angle LCH contains 90° (we drew it this way). We are seeking the angle LCE as the degrees of this angle actually represent our latitude. We need then add together the two known angles,

ECS = 23°03'
SCH = 18°26'
———
ECH = 41°29'

and subtract them from 90° to obtain the angle LCE. 90° can conveniently be expressed as 89°60'. Thus

   89°60'
− 41°29'
———
   48°31' = LCE — This is our latitude.

If we were North of the Equator and the Declination of the Sun were North at 10°, our diagram would look like this with a sextant reading of 50°.

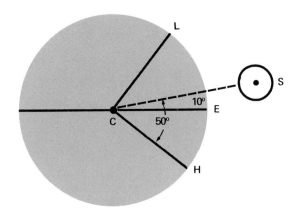

figure 25.

Here again our objective is to find LCE, as this is our latitude. We subtract the value of SCH from 90° and obtain the value of LCS.

```
  90°
 −50°   SCH
  40°   LCS
```

We then add SCE to this to obtain LCE.

```
  40°   LCS
 +10°   SCE
  50°   LCE — This is our latitude.
```

If we were South of the Equator the only change is to place H beyond the Sun as we face it.

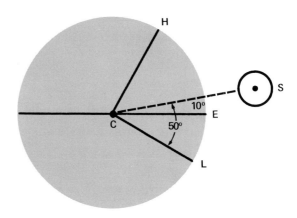

figure 26.

In essence, all we must do in each case is obtain the value of the angle LCE. The diagram may be turned in several different ways but always LCH will be a 90° angle and we will have two known angles which will form portions of it. By combining the known angles of Declination and sextant reading (H.O.) to suit our particular circumstances we will always be able to find the value of LCE, which will give us our latitude.

Remember that if we are facing South at the time of the sight, H will be South of us, below the Equator as in Figures 24 and 25. If we are facing North, H will be North of us as in Figure 26 above. Thus, L and H will always straddle the Sun line.

To avoid confusion it is important always to

draw a diagram so that the relationship of the various angles will be clear. Also, this will eliminate the need for memorizing a series of rules which tell what to do when North or South of the Equator when Declination is North or South. The diagram shows all simply and clearly, so always draw it and be sure.

In making your diagram it is not necessary to draw it with great precision, measuring angles with a protractor and such. A freehand drawing is sufficient since the diagram is merely a tool to help you visualize the relationship of the various angles and bodies. It is useful, however, to make the diagram large enough so that the numbers of the angles can be written in the actual angles and be easily read. When you are wet, cold, tired and hungry, every device that will lessen possible confusion and the resultant possible errors is important. For ease of use and clarity, an Earth Circle of at least three inches in diameter is recommended.

Plotting In plotting on a chart the latitude obtained by your noon sight calculations, measure with your dividers either North or South from the nearest whole degree parallel crossing the chart the required minutes obtained from the scale on the side of the chart. Do the same to plot the longitude except that with longitude you must measure East or West from a meridian the minutes obtained from the scale at the top or bottom of the chart.

In measuring nautical miles on a chart, always be sure to use the scale at the side rather than that at the top or bottom. The scales on the sides show latitude, the lines of which are parallel, and they are thus uniformly spaced. The top and bottom scales show longitude, the meridians of which are not parallel, and which therefore cannot be used in measuring miles.

Problems

Determine latitude as follows:
1. January 2, 1972 DR Lat. N. 42°50'
   Time of LAN 12:10:05
   Sextant reading HO 24°56'
2. January 3, 1972 DR Lat. S.30°02'
   Time of LAN 11:59:22
   Sextant reading HO 83°17'
                              (Answers on page 45.)

Time of Meridian Passage

It is possible to follow the Sun with a sextant beginning about 1130 local time and noting the zenith by taking almost constant shots up until the Sun has clearly begun to descend. However, there is a simple method of predicting the time of meridian passage and its use will make long periods of squinting through the sextant's eye piece unnecessary.

To predict the time of local apparent noon (meridian passage), begin with DR longitude and enter the GHA table for the date seeking the GHA nearest the value of your longitude but less than it. For example, on January 1, 1972, we are in the North Atlantic at DR longitude W 48°37'. Looking down the GHA column we find that at 1500 hours the Sun's GHA is 44°09.9'. We then subtract this GHA from our longitude (first rounding off the fraction to its nearest whole number for simplicity), thus 48°37'

$-44°10' = 4°27'$.

Refer now to the table of "Increments and Corrections" and look down the $\frac{Sun}{Planet}$ column until you find 4°27'. Reading to the left the value of 4°27' is shown to be 17^m48^s. This increment is then added to the 1500 hours for a total Greenwich Time of $15^h17^m48^s$.

Reference to Figure 2 will show that at longitude W 48° we are in the third time zone. Therefore, to convert from G.M.T. to local time we must subtract 3 hours. Thus, $15^h17^m48^s - 3$ hours = $12^h17^m48^s$. This should be the local time of meridian passage.

Since the DR longitude may be slightly off from the true longitude it would be well to begin observations approximately 10 minutes before the predicted time of meridian passage and to continue them until the Sun clearly has begun to descend.

Taking the Time

As noted above, the Sun is constantly moving across the sky at approximately 15° per hour. Since each hour at the Equator represents approximately 1044 miles, it is obvious that accurate time must be observed if one is to obtain a meaningful fix from a celestial observation. An error of *four seconds* in time will result in an error of *one mile* in location, so great care must be taken both in keeping and noting the time.

If someone is available to assist the navigator while he is shooting, it is helpful. The navigator can then prepare the timekeeper by stating, "Standby"; and as he makes his final adjustment, "Mark." The timekeeper should note the second, then the minutes and lastly the hour of the shot. He should then list beside the time the altitude reading from the sextant given him by the navigator.

Some navigators use a stopwatch as an aid in taking the time. The method here is to start the stopwatch at a convenient whole minute (which is noted on a work sheet) and punch it to stop and thus record the moment of when the navigator calls "Mark." The time shown on the stopwatch is then added to the original whole minute time and a very precise result obtained.

Good results can be obtained without an assistant using the same methods but care must be taken so that the result will be as accurate as possible.

As one follows the Sun for a noon sight it will rise, appear to hang for a few moments at its zenith and then begin to descend. Since it may be difficult to determine the actual second of its greatest height because of its apparent hesitation, the following will prove useful. During its ascendency, take and record as many shots as possible. Be sure to note both the time and the H.S. of each shot. Then as the Sun begins its descent, set the sextant at the same altitude that it was on for one of the ascending shots and record the time when the Sun touches the horizon at this setting. Half time between the two shots will then be the moment of meridian passage.

Moon Shots   From time to time during daylight hours both the Moon and the horizon are visible. At such times, a fix may be obtained from the Moon's meridian passage by following the same procedures as for the Sun with but one additional correction to the H.S. Also, of course, G.H.A. and Dec. are used as given for the Moon in the *Nautical Almanac.*

Because the Moon and the Earth are so close together, astronomically speaking, it does make a difference that observations cannot be made from the Earth's center. This difference of angle of observation from the Earth's surface rather than its center is known as *parallax.*

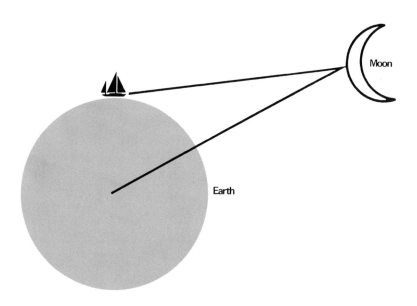

figure 27.

The last column in the Moon section of the daily pages of the *Almanac* is headed H.P. This stands for Horizontal Parallax and is an additional correction factor which must be applied to H.S. to obtain H.O.

In working a Moon sight note the time of meridian passage and the H.S. as usual. In addition, note the H.P. for the nearest whole hour to the time of the sight. Turn then to the table of Altitude Correction for the Moon inside the back cover of the *Nautical Almanac*. The correction is in two parts. The first is similar to that for the Sun as found in the front of the *Almanac* and is entered with apparent altitude. In the second, the lower part of the table is used with the given H.P. applied in the same column vertically as that from which the first correction was taken.

The two corrections from the upper and lower portions of the table are then added together and the total correction added to the apparent altitude. This then becomes the H.O.

In the event that the upper limb has been used instead of the lower limb, 30' is to be subtracted from the altitude of the upper limb.

Further instructions for the moon sight appear with the tables in the back of the *Nautical Almanac*.

Answers to Longitude Problems

1. Zone Time		12:10:05	
Zone Description	+	8	(Add ZD for West Long., Subtract ZD for East Long.)
GMT		20:10:05	

GHA of 20:00:00 hrs. =	119°01.4′	(whole hour)
	2°31.3′	(increment for 10^m05^s from table)
	W.121°32.7′	
	Say W.121°33′	

2. ZT =	11:59:22
ZD = —	4
GMT =	7:59:22

GHA of 7:00:00 hrs. =	284°12.3′	(whole hour)
	14°50.5′	(increment for 59^m22^s)
TOTAL GHA =	298°62.8′	= 299°02.5′

359°60.0′
—299°02.8′
E. 60°57.2′

To obtain East long. from GHA over 180°, subtract GHA from 360°.

1. Take Dec. from daily pages of *Nautical Almanac* for
   whole hour nearest time of LAN.

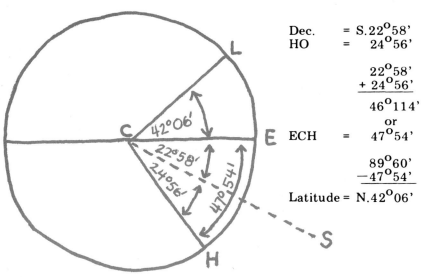

Dec. = S.22°58'
HO = 24°56'

22°58'
+ 24°56'

46°114'
or
ECH = 47°54'

89°60'
−47°54'

Latitude = N.42°06'

2.

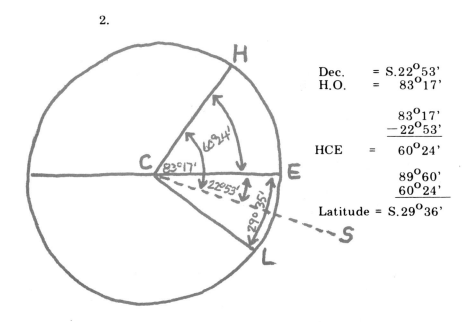

Dec. = S.22°53'
H.O. = 83°17'

83°17'
−22°53'

HCE = 60°24'

89°60'
60°24'

Latitude = S.29°36'

45

1972 JANUARY 1, 2, 3 (SAT., SUN., MON.)

SUN and MOON

G.M.T.	SUN G.H.A.	SUN Dec.	MOON G.H.A.	v	MOON Dec.	d	H.P.
1 SATURDAY							
00	179 14.4	S 23 05.5	356 54.6	5.7	N 25 01.9	6.0	58.5
01	194 14.1	05.3	11 19.3	5.9	24 55.9	6.2	58.4
02	209 13.8	05.2	25 44.2	5.9	24 49.7	6.3	58.4
03	224 13.5	05.0	40 09.1	6.1	24 43.4	6.5	58.4
04	239 13.2	04.8	54 34.2	6.2	24 36.9	6.6	58.4
05	254 12.9	04.6	68 59.4	6.2	24 30.3	6.8	58.3
06	269 12.6	S 23 04.4	83 24.6	6.4	N 24 23.5	6.9	58.3
07	284 12.3	04.2	97 50.0	6.4	24 16.6	7.1	58.3
08	299 12.0	04.0	112 15.4	6.6	24 09.5	7.2	58.3
09	314 11.7	03.8	126 41.0	6.7	24 02.3	7.3	58.2
10	329 11.4	03.6	141 06.7	6.7	23 55.0	7.5	58.2
11	344 11.1	03.4	155 32.4	6.9	23 47.5	7.6	58.2
12	359 10.8	S 23 03.3	169 58.3	7.0	N 23 39.9	7.8	58.1
13	14 10.5	03.1	184 24.3	7.1	23 32.1	7.8	58.1
14	29 10.2	02.9	198 50.4	7.2	23 24.3	8.1	58.1
15	44 09.9	02.7	213 16.6	7.3	23 16.2	8.1	58.1
16	59 09.6	02.5	227 42.9	7.4	23 08.1	8.3	58.0
17	74 09.3	02.3	242 09.3	7.6	22 59.8	8.4	58.0
18	89 09.0	S 23 02.1	256 35.9	7.6	N 22 51.4	8.5	58.0
19	104 08.8	01.9	271 02.5	7.8	22 42.9	8.7	58.0
20	119 08.5	01.7	285 29.3	7.8	22 34.2	8.8	57.9
21	134 08.2	01.5	299 56.1	8.0	22 25.4	8.8	57.9
22	149 07.9	01.3	314 23.1	8.1	22 16.6	9.1	57.9
23	164 07.6	01.1	328 50.2	8.2	22 07.5	9.1	57.8
2 SUNDAY							
00	179 07.3	S 23 00.9	343 17.4	8.3	N 21 58.4	9.2	57.8
01	194 07.0	00.7	357 44.7	8.4	21 49.2	9.3	57.8
02	209 06.7	00.5	12 12.1	8.6	21 39.8	9.5	57.7
03	224 06.4	00.2	26 39.7	8.6	21 30.3	9.6	57.7
04	239 06.1	23 00.0	41 07.3	8.8	21 20.7	9.7	57.7
05	254 05.8	22 59.8	55 35.1	8.9	21 11.0	9.8	57.7
06	269 05.5	S 22 59.6	70 03.0	9.0	N 21 01.2	9.9	57.6
07	284 05.2	59.4	84 31.0	9.1	20 51.3	10.0	57.6
08	299 04.9	59.2	98 59.1	9.2	20 41.3	10.1	57.6
09	314 04.6	59.0	113 27.3	9.4	20 31.2	10.2	57.5
10	329 04.3	58.8	127 55.7	9.4	20 21.0	10.3	57.5
11	344 04.0	58.6	142 24.1	9.6	20 10.7	10.5	57.5
12	359 03.8	S 22 58.4	156 52.7	9.7	N 20 00.3	10.5	57.4
13	14 03.5	58.1	171 21.4	9.7	19 49.8	10.6	57.4
14	29 03.2	57.9	185 50.1	10.0	19 39.2	10.7	57.4
15	44 02.9	57.7	200 19.1	10.0	19 28.5	10.8	57.4
16	59 02.6	57.5	214 48.1	10.1	19 17.7	10.9	57.3
17	74 02.3	57.3	229 17.2	10.2	19 06.8	10.9	57.3

Twilight, Sunrise, Moonrise

Lat.	Twilight Naut.	Twilight Civil	Sun-rise	Moonrise 1	2	3	4
N 72	08 24	10 42	■			17 05	19 29
N 70	08 05	09 49	■	13 43	14 36	17 36	19 42
68	07 50	09 17	■	14 41	15 42	17 59	19 53
66	07 37	08 53	10 27	15 14	16 17	18 16	20 02
64	07 27	08 34	09 49	15 39	16 42	18 31	20 10
62	07 17	08 19	09 23	15 58	17 02	18 42	20 16
60	07 09	08 05	09 02	16 14	17 18	18 52	20 21
N 58	07 02	07 54	08 45	16 28	17 31	19 01	20 26
56	06 56	07 44	08 31	16 40	17 43	19 09	20 30
54	06 50	07 36	08 18	16 50	17 53	19 16	20 34
52	06 44	07 28	08 08		18 02	19 22	20 38
50	06 39	07 20	07 58	17 12	18 10	19 27	20 41
45	06 28	07 05	07 38	17 30	18 27	19 39	20 48
N 40	06 18	06 52	07 22	17 45	18 41	19 48	20 53
35	06 09	06 40	07 08	17 58	18 52	19 57	20 58
30	06 00	06 30	06 56	18 20	19 02	20 04	21 02
20	05 44	06 11	06 35	18 39	19 20	20 17	21 10
N 10	05 28	05 54	06 17	18 56	19 35	20 27	21 16
0	05 11	05 38	06 00	19 14	19 49	20 37	21 22
S 10	04 53	05 20	05 43	19 33	20 03	20 48	21 28
20	04 31	05 00	05 24	19 54	20 18	20 58	21 34
30	04 03	04 35	05 02	20 07	20 35	21 08	21 41
35	03 44	04 20	04 50	20 21	20 45	21 17	21 46
40	03 21	04 02	04 35	20 38	20 56	21 25	21 50
45	02 51	03 40	04 17	20 59	21 10	21 35	21 56
S 50	02 08	03 11	03 55	21 09	21 26	21 46	22 02
52	01 41	02 57	03 33	21 20	21 33	21 51	22 05
54	01 01	02 39	03 19	21 33	21 41	21 56	22 08
56	///	02 18	03 03	21 48	21 51	22 03	22 12
58	///	01 50	02 43	22 05	22 01	22 11	22 16
S 60	///	01 06			22 13	22 17	22 20

Sunset, Twilight, Moonset

Lat.	Sun-set	Twilight Civil	Naut.	Moonset 1	2	3	4
N 72	■	13 26	15 44			12 10	11 20
N 70	■	14 18	16 03	11 52	12 54	11 36	11 04
68	■	14 51	16 18	10 53	11 47	11 12	10 51
66	13 40	15 15	16 30	10 19	11 10	10 53	10 40
64	14 18	15 33	16 41	09 54	10 44	10 37	10 31
62	14 45	15 49	16 50		10 07	10 24	10 24
60	15 05	16 02	16 58			10 13	10 17

(Excerpt from the *Nautical Almanac*.)

Day	SUN Eqn. of Time 00ʰ	Eqn. of Time 12ʰ	Mer. Pass.	MOON Mer. Pass. Upper	Mer. Pass. Lower	Age	Phase
	m s	m s	h m	h m	h m	d	
1	03 02	03 16	12 03	00 13	12 42	15	◯
2	03 30	03 44	12 04	01 09	13 36	16	
3	03 58	04 12	12 04	02 01	14 25	17	

| | S.D. | d | S.D. 16·3 | S.D. 15·8 | S.D. 15·7 | S.D. 15·5 | |

2^m

2^m	SUN PLANETS	ARIES	MOON	v or d	Corrn	v or d	Corrn	v or d	Corrn
s	° '	° '	° '	'	'	'	'	'	'
00	0 30·0	0 30·1	0 28·6	0·0	0·0	6·0	0·3	12·0	0·5
01	0 30·3	0 30·3	0 28·9	0·1	0·0	6·1	0·3	12·1	0·5
02	0 30·5	0 30·6	0 29·1	0·2	0·0	6·2	0·3	12·2	0·5
03	0 30·8	0 30·8	0 29·3	0·3	0·0	6·3	0·3	12·3	0·5
04	0 31·0	0 31·1	0 29·6	0·4	0·0	6·4	0·3	12·4	0·5
05	0 31·3	0 31·3	0 29·8	0·5	0·0	6·5	0·3	12·5	0·5
06	0 31·5	0 31·6	0 30·1	0·6	0·0	6·6	0·3	12·6	0·5
07	0 31·8	0 31·8	0 30·3	0·7	0·0	6·7	0·3	12·7	0·5
08	0 32·0	0 32·1	0 30·5	0·8	0·0	6·8	0·3	12·8	0·5
09	0 32·3	0 32·3	0 30·8	0·9	0·0	6·9	0·3	12·9	0·5
10	0 32·5	0 32·6	0 31·0	1·0	0·0	7·0	0·3	13·0	0·5
11	0 32·8	0 32·8	0 31·3	1·1	0·0	7·1	0·3	13·1	0·5
12	0 33·0	0 33·1	0 31·5	1·2	0·1	7·2	0·3	13·2	0·6
13	0 33·3	0 33·3	0 31·7	1·3	0·1	7·3	0·3	13·3	0·6
14	0 33·5	0 33·6	0 32·0	1·4	0·1	7·4	0·3	13·4	0·6
15	0 33·8	0 33·8	0 32·2	1·5	0·1	7·5	0·3	13·5	0·6
16	0 34·0	0 34·1	0 32·5	1·6	0·1	7·6	0·3	13·6	0·6
17	0 34·3	0 34·3	0 32·7	1·7	0·1	7·7	0·3	13·7	0·6
18	0 34·5	0 34·6	0 32·9	1·8	0·1	7·8	0·3	13·8	0·6
19	0 34·8	0 34·8	0 33·2	1·9	0·1	7·9	0·3	13·9	0·6
20	0 35·0	0 35·1	0 33·4	2·0	0·1	8·0	0·3	14·0	0·6
21	0 35·3	0 35·3	0 33·6	2·1	0·1	8·1	0·3	14·1	0·6
22	0 35·5	0 35·6	0 33·9	2·2	0·1	8·2	0·3	14·2	0·6
23	0 35·8	0 35·8	0 34·1	2·3	0·1	8·3	0·3	14·3	0·6
24	0 36·0	0 36·1	0 34·4	2·4	0·1	8·4	0·3	14·4	0·6
25	0 36·3	0 36·3	0 34·6	2·5	0·1	8·5	0·4	14·5	0·6
26	0 36·5	0 36·6	0 34·8	2·6	0·1	8·6	0·4	14·6	0·6
27	0 36·8	0 36·8	0 35·1	2·7	0·1	8·7	0·4	14·7	0·6
28	0 37·0	0 37·1	0 35·3	2·8	0·1	8·8	0·4	14·8	0·6
29	0 37·3	0 37·4	0 35·6	2·9	0·1	8·9	0·4	14·9	0·6
30	0 37·5	0 37·6	0 35·8	3·0	0·1	9·0	0·4	15·0	0·6
31	0 37·8	0 37·9	0 36·0	3·1	0·1	9·1	0·4	15·1	0·6
32	0 38·0	0 38·1	0 36·3	3·2	0·1	9·2	0·4	15·2	0·6
33	0 38·3	0 38·4	0 36·5	3·3	0·1	9·3	0·4	15·3	0·6
34	0 38·5	0 38·6	0 36·7	3·4	0·1	9·4	0·4	15·4	0·6
35	0 38·8	0 38·9	0 37·0	3·5	0·1	9·5	0·4	15·5	0·6

3^m

3^m	SUN PLANETS	ARIES	MOON	v or d	Corrn	v or d	Corrn	v or d	Corrn
s	° '	° '	° '	'	'	'	'	'	'
00	0 45·0	0 45·1	0 43·0	0·0	0·0	6·0	0·4	12·0	0·7
01	0 45·3	0 45·4	0 43·2	0·1	0·0	6·1	0·4	12·1	0·7
02	0 45·5	0 45·6	0 43·4	0·2	0·0	6·2	0·4	12·2	0·7
03	0 45·8	0 45·9	0 43·7	0·3	0·0	6·3	0·4	12·3	0·7
04	0 46·0	0 46·1	0 43·9	0·4	0·0	6·4	0·4	12·4	0·7
05	0 46·3	0 46·4	0 44·1	0·5	0·0	6·5	0·4	12·5	0·7
06	0 46·5	0 46·6	0 44·4	0·6	0·0	6·6	0·4	12·6	0·7
07	0 46·8	0 46·9	0 44·6	0·7	0·0	6·7	0·4	12·7	0·7
08	0 47·0	0 47·1	0 44·9	0·8	0·0	6·8	0·4	12·8	0·7
09	0 47·3	0 47·4	0 45·1	0·9	0·1	6·9	0·4	12·9	0·7
10	0 47·5	0 47·6	0 45·3	1·0	0·1	7·0	0·4	13·0	0·8
11	0 47·8	0 47·9	0 45·6	1·1	0·1	7·1	0·4	13·1	0·8
12	0 48·0	0 48·1	0 45·8	1·2	0·1	7·2	0·4	13·2	0·8
13	0 48·3	0 48·4	0 46·1	1·3	0·1	7·3	0·4	13·3	0·8
14	0 48·5	0 48·6	0 46·3	1·4	0·1	7·4	0·4	13·4	0·8
15	0 48·8	0 48·9	0 46·5	1·5	0·1	7·5	0·4	13·5	0·8
16	0 49·0	0 49·1	0 46·8	1·6	0·1	7·6	0·4	13·6	0·8
17	0 49·3	0 49·4	0 47·0	1·7	0·1	7·7	0·5	13·7	0·8
18	0 49·5	0 49·6	0 47·2	1·8	0·1	7·8	0·5	13·8	0·8
19	0 49·8	0 49·9	0 47·5	1·9	0·1	7·9	0·5	13·9	0·8
20	0 50·0	0 50·1	0 47·7	2·0	0·1	8·0	0·5	14·0	0·8
21	0 50·3	0 50·4	0 48·0	2·1	0·1	8·1	0·5	14·1	0·8
22	0 50·5	0 50·6	0 48·2	2·2	0·1	8·2	0·5	14·2	0·8
23	0 50·8	0 50·9	0 48·4	2·3	0·1	8·3	0·5	14·3	0·8
24	0 51·0	0 51·1	0 48·7	2·4	0·1	8·4	0·5	14·4	0·8
25	0 51·3	0 51·4	0 48·9	2·5	0·1	8·5	0·5	14·5	0·9
26	0 51·5	0 51·6	0 49·2	2·6	0·1	8·6	0·5	14·6	0·9
27	0 51·8	0 51·9	0 49·4	2·7	0·2	8·7	0·5	14·7	0·9
28	0 52·0	0 52·1	0 49·6	2·8	0·2	8·8	0·5	14·8	0·9
29	0 52·3	0 52·4	0 49·9	2·9	0·2	8·9	0·5	14·9	0·9
30	0 52·5	0 52·6	0 50·1	3·0	0·2	9·0	0·5	15·0	0·9
31	0 52·8	0 52·9	0 50·3	3·1	0·2	9·1	0·5	15·1	0·9
32	0 53·0	0 53·1	0 50·6	3·2	0·2	9·2	0·5	15·2	0·9
33	0 53·3	0 53·4	0 50·8	3·3	0·2	9·3	0·5	15·3	0·9
34	0 53·5	0 53·6	0 51·1	3·4	0·2	9·4	0·5	15·4	0·9
35	0 53·8	0 53·9	0 51·3	3·5	0·2	9·5	0·6	15·5	0·9

CONVERSION OF ARC TO TIME

0°–59°		60°–119°		120°–179°		180°–239°		240°–299°		300°–359°		′	0′·00	0′·25	0′·50	0′·75
°	h m	°	h m	°	h m	°	h m	°	h m	°	h m	′	m s	m s	m s	m s
0	0 00	60	4 00	120	8 00	180	12 00	240	16 00	300	20 00	0	0 00	0 01	0 02	0 03
1	0 04	61	4 04	121	8 04	181	12 04	241	16 04	301	20 04	1	0 04	0 05	0 06	0 07
2	0 08	62	4 08	122	8 08	182	12 08	242	16 08	302	20 08	2	0 08	0 09	0 10	0 11
3	0 12	63	4 12	123	8 12	183	12 12	243	16 12	303	20 12	3	0 12	0 13	0 14	0 15
4	0 16	64	4 16	124	8 16	184	12 16	244	16 16	304	20 16	4	0 16	0 17	0 18	0 19
5	0 20	65	4 20	125	8 20	185	12 20	245	16 20	305	20 20	5	0 20	0 21	0 22	0 23
6	0 24	66	4 24	126	8 24	186	12 24	246	16 24	306	20 24	6	0 24	0 25	0 26	0 27
7	0 28	67	4 28	127	8 28	187	12 28	247	16 28	307	20 28	7	0 28	0 29	0 30	0 31
8	0 32	68	4 32	128	8 32	188	12 32	248	16 32	308	20 32	8	0 32	0 33	0 34	0 35
9	0 36	69	4 36	129	8 36	189	12 36	249	16 36	309	20 36	9	0 36	0 37	0 38	0 39
10	0 40	70	4 40	130	8 40	190	12 40	250	16 40	310	20 40	10	0 40	0 41	0 42	0 43
11	0 44	71	4 44	131	8 44	191	12 44	251	16 44	311	20 44	11	0 44	0 45	0 46	0 47
12	0 48	72	4 48	132	8 48	192	12 48	252	16 48	312	20 48	12	0 48	0 49	0 50	0 51
13	0 52	73	4 52	133	8 52	193	12 52	253	16 52	313	20 52	13	0 52	0 53	0 54	0 55
14	0 56	74	4 56	134	8 56	194	12 56	254	16 56	314	20 56	14	0 56	0 57	0 58	0 59
15	1 00	75	5 00	135	9 00	195	13 00	255	17 00	315	21 00	15	1 00	1 01	1 02	1 03
16	1 04	76	5 04	136	9 04	196	13 04	256	17 04	316	21 04	16	1 04	1 05	1 06	1 07
17	1 08	77	5 08	137	9 08	197	13 08	257	17 08	317	21 08	17	1 08	1 09	1 10	1 11
18	1 12	78	5 12	138	9 12	198	13 12	258	17 12	318	21 12	18	1 12	1 13	1 14	1 15
19	1 16	79	5 16	139	9 16	199	13 16	259	17 16	319	21 16	19	1 16	1 17	1 18	1 19
20	1 20	80	5 20	140	9 20	200	13 20	260	17 20	320	21 20	20	1 20	1 21	1 22	1 23
21	1 24	81	5 24	141	9 24	201	13 24	261	17 24	321	21 24	21	1 24	1 25	1 26	1 27
22	1 28	82	5 28	142	9 28	202	13 28	262	17 28	322	21 28	22	1 28	1 29	1 30	1 31
23	1 32	83	5 32	143	9 32	203	13 32	263	17 32	323	21 32	23	1 32	1 33	1 34	1 35
24	1 36	84	5 36	144	9 36	204	13 36	264	17 36	324	21 36	24	1 36	1 37	1 38	1 39
25	1 40	85	5 40	145	9 40	205	13 40	265	17 40	325	21 40	25	1 40	1 41	1 42	1 43
26	1 44	86	5 44	146	9 44	206	13 44	266	17 44	326	21 44	26	1 44	1 45	1 46	1 47
27	1 48	87	5 48	147	9 48	207	13 48	267	17 48	327	21 48	27	1 48	1 49	1 50	1 51
28	1 52	88	5 52	148	9 52	208	13 52	268	17 52	328	21 52	28	1 52	1 53	1 54	1 55
29	1 56	89	5 56	149	9 56	209	13 56	269	17 56	329	21 56	29	1 56	1 57	1 58	1 59
30	2 00	90	6 00	150	10 00	210	14 00	270	18 00	330	22 00	30	2 00	2 01	2 02	2 03
31	2 04	91	6 04	151	10 04	211	14 04	271	18 04	331	22 04	31	2 04	2 05	2 06	2 07
32	2 08	92	6 08	152	10 08	212	14 08	272	18 08	332	22 08	32	2 08	2 09	2 10	2 11
33	2 12	93	6 12	153	10 12	213	14 12	273	18 12	333	22 12	33	2 12	2 13	2 14	2 15
34	2 16	94	6 16	154	10 16	214	14 16	274	18 16	334	22 16	34	2 16	2 17	2 18	2 19